[SURVIVING]
THE IMPOSSIBLE

SURVIVING
A VAMPIRE
INVASION

MADELINE TYLER

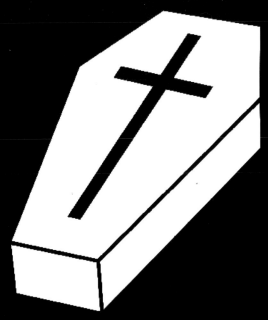

 Gareth Stevens
PUBLISHING

Please visit our website, www.garethstevens.com.
For a free color catalog of all our high-quality books, call toll free 1-800-542-2595
or fax 1-877-542-2596.

Cataloging-in-Publication Data

Names: Tyler, Madeline.
Title: Surviving a vampire invasion / Madeline Tyler.
Description: New York : Gareth Stevens Publishing, 2019. | Series: Surviving the impossible |
Includes glossary and index.
Identifiers: ISBN 9781538235140 (pbk.) | ISBN 9781538235164 (library bound) | ISBN
9781538235157 (6pack)
Subjects: LCSH: Vampires--Juvenile literature. | Survival--Juvenile literature.
Classification: LCC GR830.V3 T95 2019 | DDC 398.21--dc23

First Edition

Published in 2019 by
Gareth Stevens Publishing
111 East 14th Street, Suite 349
New York, NY 10003

© 2019 Booklife Publishing
This edition is published by arrangement with Booklife Publishing

Written by: Madeline Tyler
Edited by: John Wood
Designed by: Drue Rintoul

Printed in the United States of America

CPSIA compliance information: Batch #CW19GS: For further information, contact Gareth Stevens, New York, New York at 1-800-542-2595

CONTENTS

Words that look like THIS can be found in the glossary on page 31.

THE UPRISING

You may not realize it, but vampires are living among us right now, and have been for thousands of years. Vampires are very intelligent and can be difficult to DETECT. They are careful not to draw attention to themselves and mostly live in the countryside, away from large groups of people.

They usually hunt two or three times a week and can survive on just animal blood if they need to. However, drinking only animal blood every day would be like eating vegetables for every meal – it would get very boring. A vampire actually wants a different type of blood – human blood!

Vampires might risk their lives to sneak into towns and villages in search of tasty PREY. They may do this either alone or as part of a larger COVEN, but either way they always try to DISGUISE their hunting to look like animal attacks. Are people mysteriously dying in your town from bear or wolf attacks? Are the bodies found with bite marks on their necks and drained of their blood? If they are, these are probably vampire attacks!

VAMPIRES IN HISTORY

Grown-ups might tell you that vampires don't exist, but people have been trying to warn us about the bloodsucking monsters for hundreds and even thousands of years. Vampires have appeared in **CULTURES** all around the world, in **LEGENDS** that tell the story of evil demons that are neither dead nor alive. The demons appear as beautiful men and women who suck the blood from their victims. The stories and names may be different each time, but the message is clear in all of them – never get too close to any of these monsters!

The legend of Brahmaparusha is famous in India. In some stories, Brahmaparusha hangs upside down from trees – just like a bat – and preys on humans for their blood. It drains the blood of its victim into a human skull, which it then uses as a cup to drink from – delicious! However, Brahmaparusha is a very thirsty creature, so the blood of one human is not nearly enough to satisfy it. It could go through ten different humans and still not be full. When it is finally finished, Brahmaparusha performs a **RITUAL** dance.

Another nasty creature that you probably wouldn't want to come across is the vrykolakas. Vrykolakas are evil creatures that exist in Greek FOLKLORE. Vrykolakas are undead beings that leave their graves to roam around nearby towns. They drink so much blood that their bodies swell up and their skin turns red. Some vrykolakas are just TRICKSTERS who scare the local people and cause trouble, but others are deadlier and more dangerous. Occasionally, vrykolakas will knock on the doors of houses and call out the names of people inside. As long as you don't answer the door after one knock, the vrykolakas will leave you in peace. However, if you do answer the door to a vrykolakas, you will almost certainly die a few days later. You have been warned!

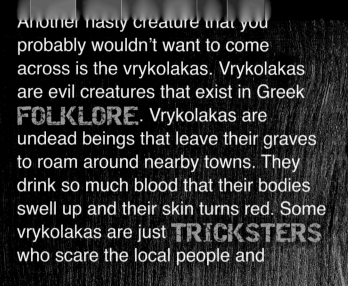

Count Dracula's castle is called Castle Dracula. It's deep in the mountains of Transylvania.

You may not have heard of Brahmaparusha or vrykolakas before, but you will almost definitely recognize this name. One of the most famous vampires in the world is Count Dracula, a mysterious **NOBLEMAN** from Transylvania. Dracula is very old and intelligent, and can transform himself into a bat, a wolf, and even fog, or mist. He is extremely pale and doesn't have a shadow or a reflection, which helps him to sneak up on his victims. Dracula also has two sharp fangs which he uses to bite into the necks of poor, unsuspecting humans.

HOW TO SPOT A VAMPIRE

Vampires are extremely quick and cunning, so it's important that you can spot one at a moment's notice. Could you tell the difference between a vampire and a man with pale skin who just likes the dark? Does your best friend have fangs, or do they just really need braces? Recognizing the signs of a vampire is a very important skill that you will need to perfect before you become a full-fledged vampire SLAYER! When the vampire uprising begins, there will be no room for mistakes.

Watch out! Vampires can be anywhere.

EYES

Vampires look very similar to ordinary humans, but one thing that gives a vampire away is its eyes. Most vampires usually have very dark brown or black eyes, but when a vampire is hungry for blood and hunting for its next meal, its eyes will turn red and glow. Sometimes just the smell of human blood is enough to turn a vampire's eyes red and send it into a FRENZY. If you ever see someone with blood-red eyes and a watering mouth approaching you, run away as fast as you can!

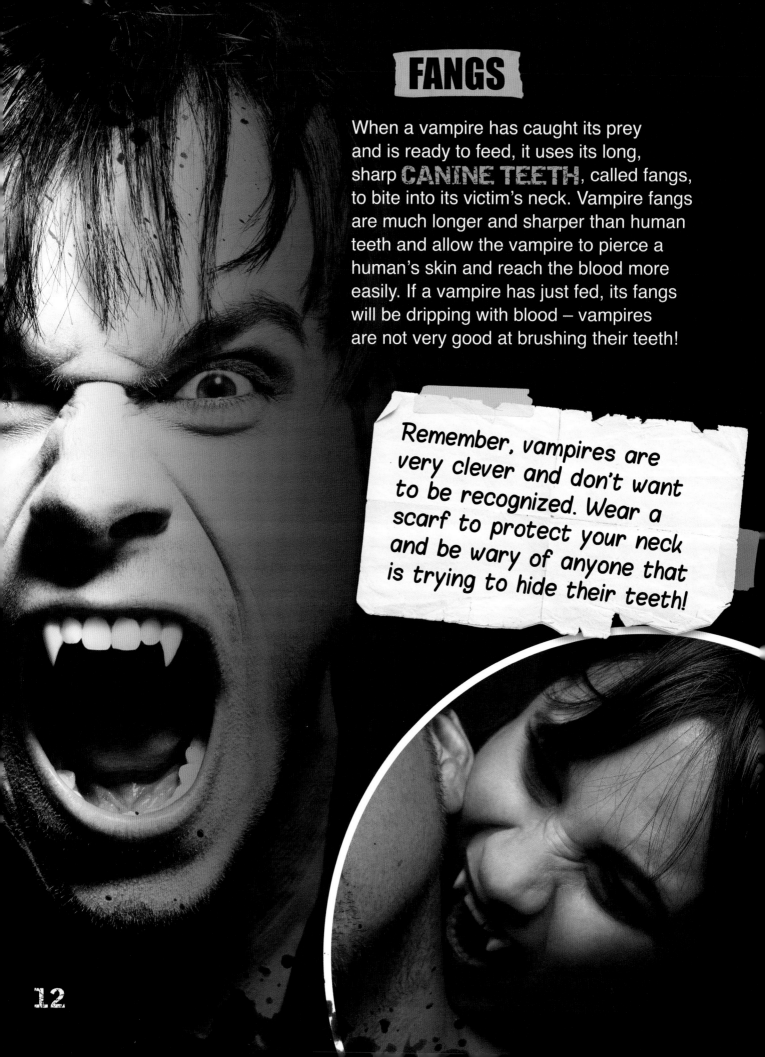

FANGS

When a vampire has caught its prey and is ready to feed, it uses its long, sharp CANINE TEETH, called fangs, to bite into its victim's neck. Vampire fangs are much longer and sharper than human teeth and allow the vampire to pierce a human's skin and reach the blood more easily. If a vampire has just fed, its fangs will be dripping with blood – vampires are not very good at brushing their teeth!

Remember, vampires are very clever and don't want to be recognized. Wear a scarf to protect your neck and be wary of anyone that is trying to hide their teeth!

SMELL

If you get close enough to a vampire to see its teeth, then you will probably also notice a foul, rotting smell. The stench is so bad that it might make you gag, or even want to be sick. This smell is made by the vampire's undead body, which may have started to rot, as well as its bloody breath and blood-stained teeth. Vampires spend a lot of their time sleeping in coffins, so they might also smell dusty or earthy. Some vampires keep their coffins in old, empty castles while others can be found underground in graveyards. Vampires are slowly learning to disguise these smells by using mouthwash and perfume, so remember to always look out for the other features of a vampire, and never let your guard down.

Don't be fooled.
Even after it has fed,
a vampire is still very
dangerous. Stay out of
danger by avoiding all
vampire encounters.

SKIN

One thing that a vampire would struggle to disguise is
its skin. Vampires stay out of the sun, so their skin is very
pale – so pale, in fact, that it is almost TRANSPARENT.
Their skin is also as cold as ice and may feel like MARBLE
to touch. After a feed, the vampire's body will swell, and their
skin will become very tight and turn slightly red. A swollen,
red vampire is the safest to be around. They won't be too
hungry and may, if you're lucky, let you escape unharmed.

14

CLOTHING

Vampires have taken to wearing lots of layers of clothes to try to keep their skin warm. However, most vampires are hundreds of years old, so many of them struggle to keep up with modern culture, especially anything to do with fashion. In fact, many vampires never change their clothes and wear the same outfit that they were wearing when they died. This can make vampires look very old-fashioned, as if they have just stepped out of an old, black-and-white movie. Male vampires are often seen wearing fancy suits and long, velvet-lined capes while female vampires wear big dresses with lots of jewelry. If you see anyone wearing old-fashioned clothing, and they're not on their way to a party or a film set, then keep your distance; they could be a vampire!

PLACES TO AVOID

Although being able to identify a vampire is a very useful skill, it should only be used as a final RESORT. The best way to avoid a vampire attack is to keep out of their way and stay as far away as possible from their homes and hangout spots.

TRANSYLVANIA

Many vampires, including Dracula, begin their lives (and afterlives) in Transylvania, an area in the European country of Romania. A long stretch of mountains called the Carpathians runs through Romania. Hundreds of years ago, Romanian vampires built lots of castles high up in the Carpathians, where they could stay hidden away from humans until they got thirsty…

Transylvania has the highest population of vampires in the world so, if you live anywhere near there – or are thinking of taking a trip there – you should definitely keep reading this book. You'll need to be battle-ready just in case any locals think you'd make a tasty treat.

CASTLES

If you don't live in Transylvania, you shouldn't relax just yet. Although most vampires stay in their homeland, in the case of a vampire invasion they will become more adventurous and travel to faraway countries in search of new, EXOTIC-tasting humans. In fact, vampire invaders are becoming more and more common, with some recently spotted in China, Russia, and Canada. These vampires usually move into large, abandoned castles that remind them of their homes in Transylvania. They try very hard not to draw attention to themselves, so the castles may still appear to be empty even after a vampire has moved in.

Look out for any movement around the castle after sunset and make sure you look up to check for any vampire bats that may be flying above your head.

GRAVEYARDS

Some vampires prefer the traditional, rustic setting of a graveyard. They stay in a coffin deep underground during the day but come out at night after the sun has set. Sunlight is very harmful to vampires, so graveyards are only safe to visit during the daytime. Have you ever walked through a graveyard at night and felt a shiver down your spine, or a cold breath on your neck? This is a sure sign of a vampire sneaking up behind you to see if it can get away with taking a sneaky bite or two. Remember, you've been warned.

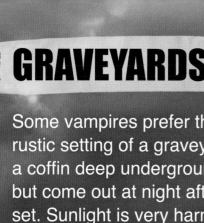

CAVES

As you probably know, vampires can transform into bats whenever they choose. This makes a great disguise and can also be useful when they need to travel long distances. Bats are expert flyers, but after very long journeys they get quite tired. They like to rest during the day by hanging upside down in dark caves. Not all bats are vampires, but unless you're a trained vampire expert, it's almost impossible to tell the difference between them. Caves and dark tunnels are the best places to catch vampires off guard, but before you launch a full-scale attack, you need to know which weapons can cause the most damage.

GATHERING WEAPONS

So now you know where vampires are most commonly found, but during a vampire invasion, they could turn up where you least expect it. You need to be prepared just in case a vampire appears on your street or in your school. Having the right weapons could mean the difference between life and death.

The best weapons for vampire-hunting are small, lightweight, and can be easily hidden. Some of the weapons you need might be hard to find, so try looking around your house for supplies that you might be able to use.

GARLIC

While you're getting your weapons together and preparing for the possible invasion, you will need to protect yourself from any vampires that may try to take you by surprise. One trick that vampire slayers throughout history have used to ward off vampires is garlic. Yes, you read that right – garlic. Garlic is very smelly, and vampires hate it! Wear a string of garlic cloves around your neck while you get your weapons ready. For extra protection, you can also dab garlic oil on your forehead and wrists. No vampire will want to come anywhere near you while you smell so strongly – just beware, stinking of garlic can ward off your fellow humans, too! Quickly have a look around your kitchen; you may have some garlic that you can wear now.

You can never have too much garlic.

WOODEN STAKE

Unfortunately, vampires can't be killed by things like regular gunshot wounds or from a whack with a baseball bat on the head. They're incredibly strong and almost indestructible, so you'll need to learn a few of their weaknesses. Vampires can heal very quickly from most injuries, but their skin and bones are still just as fragile as a human's. If you're fast enough, you should be able to kill a vampire before it has a chance to heal. One of the most effective vampire-killing methods is a wooden stake through the heart. The stake can be made from any piece of wood that has a sharp, pointy end, but the deadliest stakes are made using wood from a hawthorn tree.

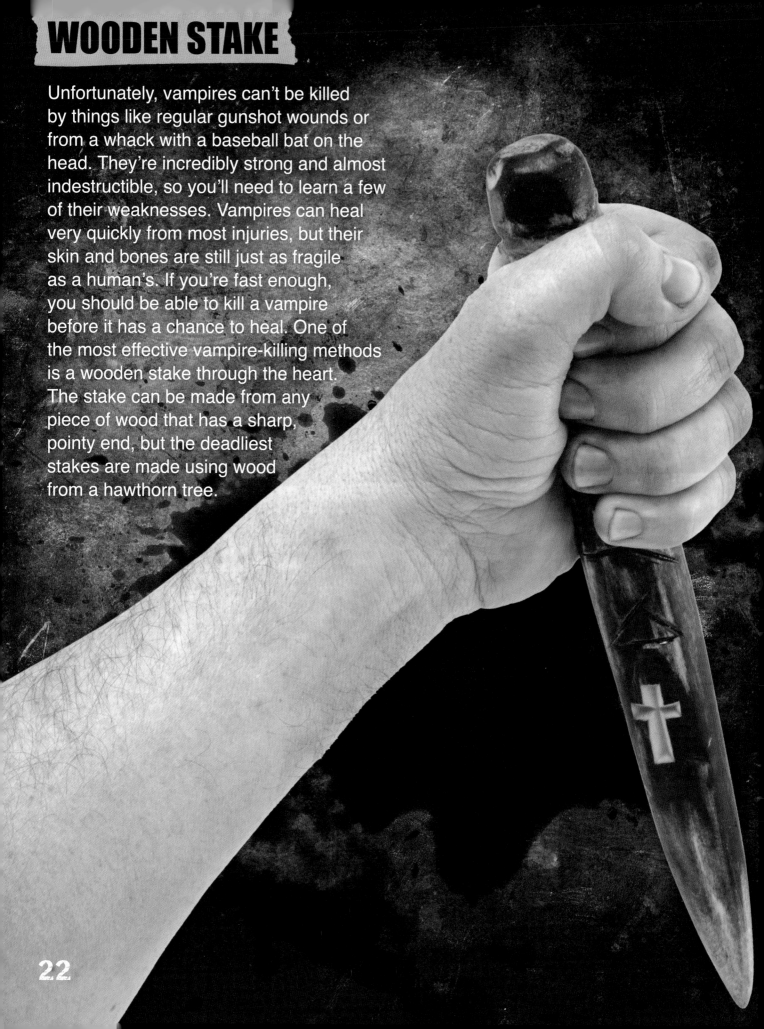

SILVER BULLETS

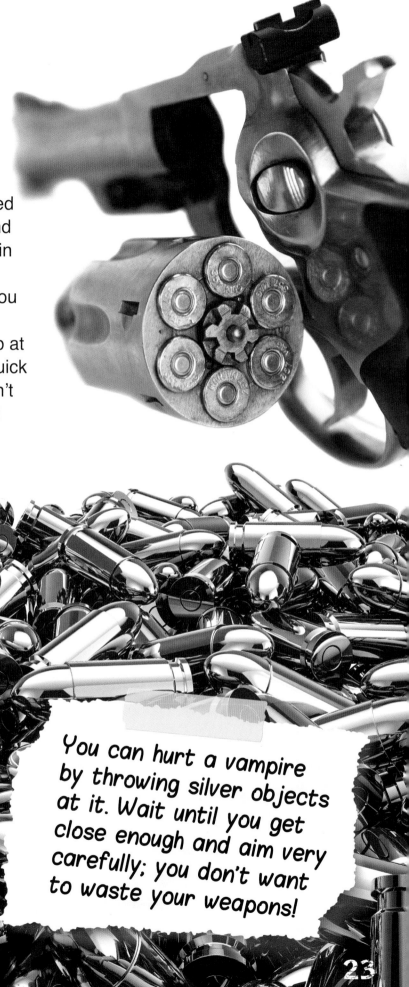

One weapon that will be harder to find is a silver bullet. If you don't happen to have any silver bullets laying around in your house, don't panic; anything made from silver will do the job. Vampires are burned by solid silver, and both jewelry and silver cutlery can inflict enough pain to slow one down. Although silver doesn't kill a vampire, it can buy you enough time to think of your next move, whether this is taking a stab at the vampire's heart or making a quick escape to your hideout. You haven't found a hideout yet?! Quick! Read about them on the next page.

You can hurt a vampire by throwing silver objects at it. Wait until you get close enough and aim very carefully; you don't want to waste your weapons!

23

CHOOSING A HIDEOUT

If you're going to survive a vampire invasion, then you'll need a base where you can safely hide from danger for as long as you need to. Your hideout should be far away from castles, caves, and graveyards, and anywhere else that you think bats and vampires may be lurking. The best locations for a hideout are hot places that get lots of sunlight. Large, open spaces are also perfect because this makes it much harder for a vampire to sneak up on you.

Always try to stay in large groups during a vampire invasion. Maybe you could share a hideout with your friends and family.

Once you have chosen your perfect hideout, stock up on food, water, and weapons and then lock all the doors and windows. For extra security, decorate the hideout with as much garlic as you can find. Hanging garlic in all doorways and windows will stop any vampires from coming inside and will keep you protected for longer.

You should also make sure that you have as many mirrors as possible in your hideout. Vampires don't have reflections, so you can use the mirrors to make sure that no one entering your hideout is secretly a vampire. Maybe place one near your main entrance so you can check as people come through the door.

25

HOW TO KILL A VAMPIRE

Hopefully, if you've chosen your hideout carefully, it will be strong enough to keep you safe for at least the first few weeks of a vampire invasion. However, when your supplies begin running low, and your garlic has gone moldy, you may have to venture outside to make a quick visit to the nearest shop. Always go out in a group and take plenty of wooden stakes and silver objects, as well as any other useful objects you may have, like knives and rope. Vampires are also sensitive to holy objects like the Bible, CRUCIFIXES, and holy water, so try carrying a few of these around with you on your trip. Before you leave, make some time to say your goodbyes. You may not be coming back… unless you read all the tips in this book, of course.

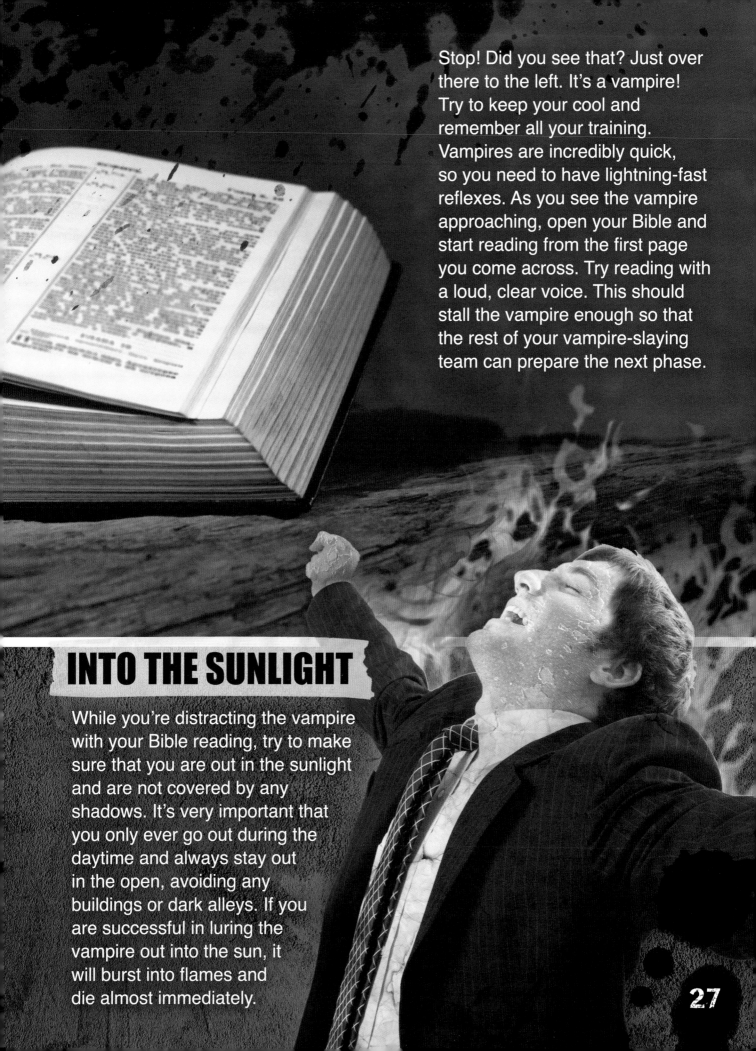

Stop! Did you see that? Just over there to the left. It's a vampire! Try to keep your cool and remember all your training. Vampires are incredibly quick, so you need to have lightning-fast reflexes. As you see the vampire approaching, open your Bible and start reading from the first page you come across. Try reading with a loud, clear voice. This should stall the vampire enough so that the rest of your vampire-slaying team can prepare the next phase.

INTO THE SUNLIGHT

While you're distracting the vampire with your Bible reading, try to make sure that you are out in the sunlight and are not covered by any shadows. It's very important that you only ever go out during the daytime and always stay out in the open, avoiding any buildings or dark alleys. If you are successful in luring the vampire out into the sun, it will burst into flames and die almost immediately.

STRAIGHT THROUGH THE HEART

Most vampires are too clever to be tricked. If this is the case for your encounter, you will have to brave the shadows. Grab your wooden stake in one hand and hold a crucifix in the other. You need to get close enough to reach the vampire's heart, but this is easier said than done. As you get closer, throw some holy water over the vampire. The vampire will be so worried about getting burned by the water that you should have enough time to take aim with your wooden stake and drive it right through its heart. Make sure you leave the stake in, because this will stop the vampire from healing and recovering.

OFF WITH ITS HEAD!

So hopefully by now, your vampire friend should be very weak. Although it's probably dying, there's still a chance that it could recover from its injuries. To make this impossible, you will need to cut off the vampire's head. Grab something sharp, like one of the knives you packed, and take the head off with one, clean swipe. The vampire might beg you to stop or try to convince you that it's changed its ways, but you mustn't trust it. Vampires are evil and bloodthirsty and can never become good again. Stay strong and go for it!

29

SURVIVING THE VAMPIRE INVASION

If you manage to destroy the vampire and escape unharmed, you may be able to quickly stock up on supplies and race back to your hideout before sunset. Hang up your fresh garlic and give yourself a pat on the back. If everyone made it back safely and there are no intruders, then you can sit back and settle down – it's going to be a long few months...

Unless you're prepared to go out and fight every vampire one by one, you'll need to wait out the invasion from the safety of your hideout. Towards the end, the vampires may start running out of humans and become desperate. They might risk coming out in the sun to launch an attack on your hideout. As long as the doors are locked, and you still have all your garlic and holy water, you'll have nothing to worry about.

KEEP OUT

GLOSSARY

CANINE TEETH	long, sharp teeth in the top of the mouth
COVEN	a group of individuals, usually vampires, with similar interests or ideas
CRUCIFIXES	images or models used in Christianity that show Jesus Christ on the cross
CULTURES	the traditions, ideas, and ways of life of groups of people
DETECT	spot or identify
DISGUISE	hide what you really look like, so you can't be recognized
EXOTIC	from a new or foreign place
FOLKLORE	the traditional culture of a group of people that is passed on by word of mouth
FRENZY	the state of being very excited or angry to the point of losing control
LEGENDS	stories from a long time ago that have been passed down
MARBLE	a type of stone that is usually hard and shiny
NOBLEMAN	a man who is part of the highest social class
PREY	animals, or people, that are hunted for food
RESORT	option
RITUAL	an ordered action that usually takes place during a religious ceremony
SLAYER	killer
TRANSPARENT	a material that lets light pass through it, causing it to be see-through
TRICKSTERS	people who play tricks

INDEX